D0495722

NORTHWEST
HIGHLANDS

A LANDSCAPE FASHIONED BY GEOLOGY

SCOTTISH NATURAL HERITAGE

©Scottish Natural Heritage 2001

ISBN 1 85397 139 1

A CIP record is held at the British Library

NP2K0907

Acknowledgements

Authors: John Mendum (BGS), Jon Merritt (BGS) and Alan McKirdy (SNH)

Series editor: Alan McKirdy (SNH).

Text on pages 38 & 39 by Alison Grant

Photography

BGS 5 top, 35, **L. Campbell** 30 centre left, 30 right, **J. Charity/SNH** 22 top, **J. Finlay** back page, **L. Gill/SNH** cover, frontispiece, 4, 8, 9, 10, 11, 12, 13, 15 top, 15 bottom, 17, 18, 19 top, 19 bottom, 20, 21 top, 21 bottom, 22 bottom, 23, 26, 27, 28, 29, 31 top, 32, 33, 34 top, 34 bottom, 36, 37, 38, 39, **J. Hyde/B&C Alexander** 24, **Lapworth Museum of Geology, University of Birmingham** 5 bottom, **N. McIntyre** 30 centre right, 30 left, **P&A. Macdonald/SNH** 14, **The Trustees of the National Museums of Scotland** 31 bottom.

Illustrations

BGS 17, **R. Bonson** 6, 7, **C. Ellery** 2, 3, 16, 25,

Further copies of this book and other publications can be obtained from:

The Publications Section,

Scottish Natural Heritage,

Battleby, Redgorton, Perth PH1 3EW

Tel 01738 444177 Fax:01738 827411

E-mail: pubs@snh.gov.uk

Web site: http://www.snh.org.uk

Cover image:

Suilven - Torridonian Sandstone

overlies Lewisian Gneiss

NORTHWEST HIGHLANDS

A Landscape Fashioned by Geology

by

John Mendum, Jon Merritt and Alan McKirdy

Loch Glencoul and Stac of Glencoul by Benjamin Peach (from Landscape Sketches by a Victorian geologist)

Contents

The Northwest Highlands of Scotland, an ancient bulwark to Atlantic storms, boast spectacular mountain and coastal scenery and large areas of exposed bedrock. This sparsely populated yet readily accessible area possesses a diverse geological character, making it a classic region where one feels closer to geology and landscape than probably anywhere else in Britain. It has been the birthplace of major geological ideas that have been applied throughout the world. This book only scratches the surface of the accumulated geological knowledge of the Northwest Highlands, but hopefully provides a new insight into how its geological development has resulted in the magnificent landscape.

The Northwest Highlands Through Time

RECENT TIMES

1,500 years. Land improvements take place with forest clearance and farming. Enhanced gulley formation occurs on mountainsides.

QUATERNARY PERIOD
THE "ICE AGE"
2.4 million years ago up to and including recent times

5,000 years. Sea level begins falling towards that of the present day.
6,000 years. Peat begins to accumulate as climate becomes wetter. Man begins clearing woodland.
8,000 years. Sea level rises, forming beaches up to 10m above present day levels. Hunter-gatherers arrive and inhabit the land.
10,000 years. Establishment of woodland whilst sea level falls well below present level.
11,500 years. Climate warms up very rapidly. Landslides and rock falls commonly occur as ground thaws.
12,500 years. Climate gradually becomes very cold. Corrie glaciers and mountain ice fields develop again. Freeze-thaw processes affect the landscape.
14,700 years. Climate warms rapidly with summer temperatures like those today. Glaciers retreat rapidly whilst sea level is up to 40m higher than today.
22,000 years. Ice now covers all but a few mountain tops and extends at least 100km west of the Scottish mainland.
29,000 years. Climate cools, snow accumulates rapidly, and the last major glaciation (Late Devensian) begins.
132,000 years. The last interglacial period begins, warmer than today, followed by 90,000 years or so of mainly Siberian conditions.
2.4 million years. Climate cools and 'Ice Age' begins.

TERTIARY PERIOD
65 to 2.4 million years ago

North Atlantic Ocean continues to widen. Volcanoes are active on Skye and Mull, with great outpourings of lava. Present day river systems established on a gently undulating plateau tilted towards the east. Evidence for tropical conditions is widespread, but climate gradually cools as the 'Ice Age' approaches.

CRETACEOUS PERIOD
65 to 142 million years ago

High sea levels prevail. Warm shallow temperate seas fringe the low-lying land, with chalk deposited across Scotland, but later removed by erosion.

JURASSIC PERIOD
142 to 206 million years ago

Opening of the North Atlantic Ocean begins. Climate on land is warm and humid. Offshore, mudstone, limestone and sandstone are deposited. Sea levels are considerably higher than today.

TRIASSIC
206 to 248 million years ago

PERMIAN
248 to 290 million years

No record of any geological events in the Northwest Highlands. Evidence for desert conditions preserved elsewhere. Offshore, sandstone, siltstone and mudstone deposited in fault-bounded basins.

CARBONIFEROUS
290 to 354 million years

No record of any geological events in the Northwest Highlands. Scotland sits astride the equator. Warm shallow seas fringe the land; reefs build up offshore.

DEVONIAN
354 to 417 million years

No record of any geological events in the Northwest Highlands. Offshore, sandstones deposited. Wide coastal plain, fringed by sand dunes and desert. Freshwater lakes existed which teemed with primitive fish life, now fossilised.

SILURIAN
417 to 443 million years

Scotland collides with Baltica (Norway and Sweden) and Avalonia (England) as the Iapetus Ocean finally closes. In the Northwest Highlands, the Moine Thrust Belt is initiated along with general uplift to create the Highlands.

ORDOVICIAN
443 to 490 million years

End of Durness Limestone deposition and first main phases of the formation of the Caledonian Mountains take place.

CAMBRIAN
490 to 545 million years

Quartzites, siltstones and Durness limestones laid down as beach or near-shore deposits on the fringes of the Laurentian continent; the Pipe Rock preserves evidence of early life in the form of trumpet-shaped worm burrows.

PRECAMBRIAN
545 to 3,5000 million years

The oldest rocks in Scotland are the Lewisian gneisses, which are interpreted as part of the Earth's crust as it existed up to three billion years ago. The Moine rocks started life as layer upon layer of sandstone, later to be altered by deep burial in the Earth's crust. Torridonian sandstones accumulated at much the same time, deposited by braided river systems, and have remained largely unaltered.

Geological Map
of the Northwest
Highlands

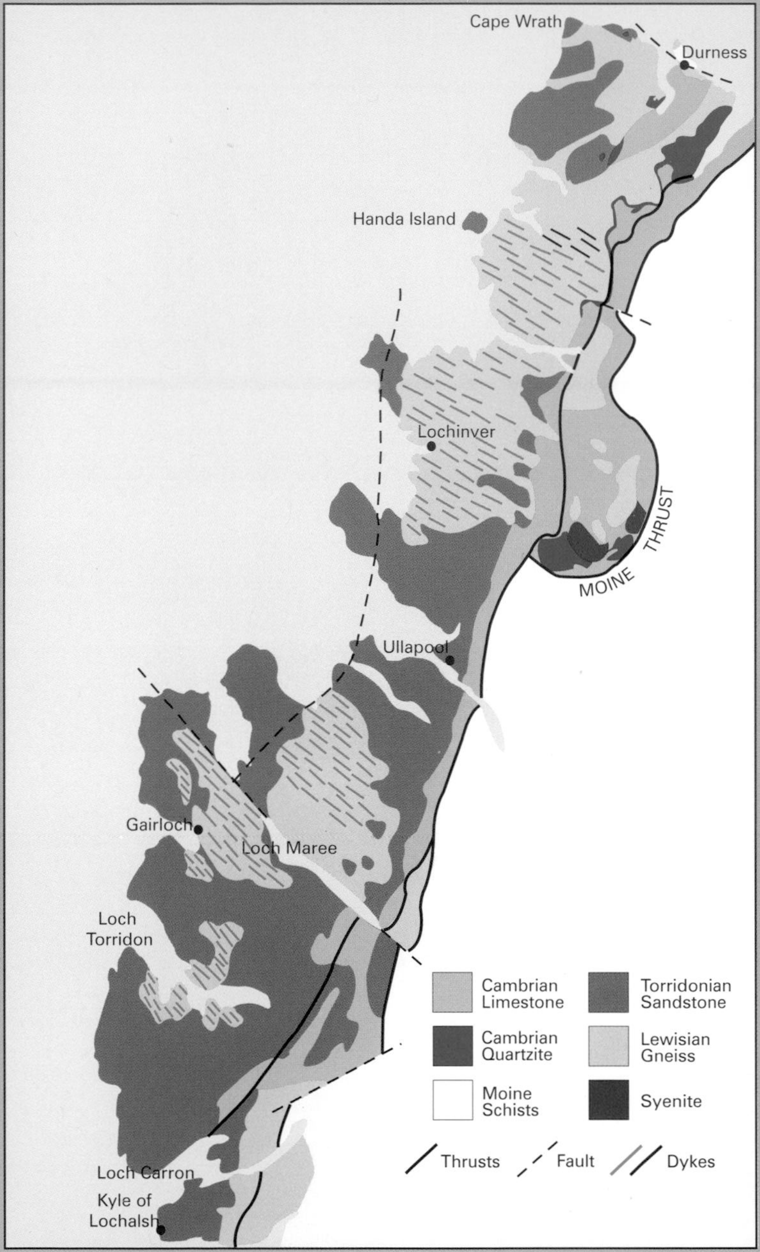

Cape Wrath
Durness
Handa Island
Lochinver
MOINE   THRUST
Ullapool
Gairloch
Loch Maree
Loch
Torridon
Loch Carron
Kyle of
Lochalsh

Cambrian
Limestone

Cambrian
Quartzite

Moine
Schists

Torridonian
Sandstone

Lewisian
Gneiss

Syenite

Thrusts   Fault   Dykes

Victorian Scientific Pioneers - The Great Debate

The Victorian era ushered in the age of the professional scientist. The general population took more interest in their natural surroundings and it was a time of empirical observation, classification, and structured reasoning. In geology, this upsurge of interest led to the perceived need for careful geological mapping of much of the country. New methods, such as viewing translucent slices of rock through a microscope, were employed as concerted attempts were made to understand the processes involved in creating the Highlands of Scotland.

Sir Roderick Impey Murchison, a Scot educated at Durham and the Royal Military College, became interested in geology, following service in the army in the Napoleonic Peninsular War. In his lifetime, he wrote over 100 scientific papers and books, travelled widely abroad, and named and defined the Silurian, Permian and Devonian systems of rocks. In 1855 aged 63 he was appointed Director-General of the Geological Survey of Great Britain. In the same year Archibald Geikie, aged 20, yet already a recognised geologist, was appointed to map rocks in Scotland. In 1860 Geikie accompanied Murchison on a tour of the Northwest Highlands, noting the hard, crystalline rocks, known as the Moine Schists, overlying the Cambrian and Ordovician fossil-bearing sediments in an apparently normal sequence. James Nicol, professor at Aberdeen, disputed this interpretation, claiming that there must be a steep faulted contact between the assumed older Moine schists and the younger sediments. Murchison died in 1871 and Nicol in 1879 with the debate still unresolved.

Peach and Horne seated outside the Inchnadamph Hotel

Charles Lapworth, a schoolmaster who had taught in Galashiels and at Madras College, St. Andrews, also made an important contribution to the debate. Having worked out the basic structure of the Southern Uplands, he then turned his attention to the Northwest Highlands in 1882 and 1883. He mapped the Durness to Loch Eriboll area and identified the basic rock structures that Peach and Horne later elucidated in great detail. Foremost amongst his discoveries was the existence of a low-angle fault or thrust, separating the Moine from the younger rocks below.

Archibald Geikie, appointed as Director-General of the Geological Survey in 1882, sent Benjamin Peach and John Horne to survey the area in more detail. Peach and Horne soon declared that Lapworth's interpretation was indeed correct and in the magazine *Nature* in 1884 they published an account of the geology that finally settled the controversy. Geikie wrote a preface referring to "prodigious terrestrial displacements" so large that 'overlying schists have certainly been thrust westward across all other rocks for at least 10 miles'. This interpretation was a revelation as it opened up a range of new possibilities to explain the way in which landscapes are formed. The careful geological mapping carried out by Peach and Horne and their colleagues in the 1880s laid the foundations for research work that continues to this day.

Charles Lapworth

Scotland's Journey

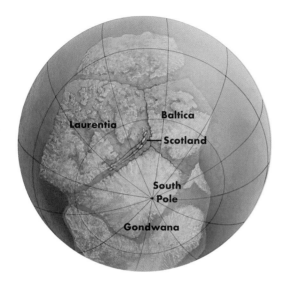

600 Million Years

A supercontinent situated around the South Pole starts to break up into individual plates. Scotland lies at the edge of Laurentia, a continental plate that also includes North America and Greenland.

500 Million Years

Laurentia has drifted northwards to tropical latitudes as the Iapetus Ocean opened. Volcanic arcs develop above subduction zones and subsequently collide with Laurentia. Avalonia (England and Wales) begins its rapid journey north, and Baltica (Norway and Sweden) spins slowly northwards.

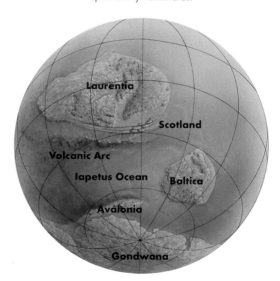

Continents have parted, collided and split asunder in a multitude of configurations since the formation of our planet four and a half billion years ago. Unlikely though it may seem, the landmass we now recognise as Scotland has journeyed extensively across the globe during its turbulent geological past. Around 600 million years ago, Scotland was located close to the South Pole and has drifted ever-northwards since that time. On its wanderings it has passed through all of the Earth's climatic zones. Evidence for deep oceans, scorching deserts and the remains of a wealth of plants and animals, most now long extinct, are all faithfully recorded in our fragmentary rock archive - the landscape around us. One of the most amazing facts about our geological past is that Scotland was separated from England and Wales during much of their early history by an ocean, once as wide as the North Atlantic. This ocean, named Iapetus after the father of Atlas, has of course long disappeared, but it existed between about 570 and 430 million years ago. At that time Scotland was still part of North America - the Laurentian continent - and lay south of the equator. The seaway which existed between the converging continents narrowed until they collided and subsequently mountains were created in place of the vanished ocean. Scotland still carries the legacy of these events. The Highlands are the eroded roots of that mountain belt formed when these continents collided.

Since late Devonian times Scotland has drifted progressively northwards through equitorial latitudes with various global dancing partners. Up to Jurassic times it formed part of large continental masses called Laurussia and Pangaea. Pangaea was a global supercontinent which only began to break up in the Jurassic with the opening of the central part of the embryo Atlantic Ocean. Scotland subsequently joined its current continental companions, collectively called Eurasia only some 65 million years ago. At that time, opening of the northern part of the Atlantic Ocean caused it to drift eastwards away from America, Canada and Greenland, to whom it had been attached for the previous 1000 million years. The separation was marked by great outpourings of basalt lavas.

40 Million Years
The North Atlantic Ocean opens 80 million years ago and at 65 million years, Greenland splits off from Europe. North America and Europe continue to drift apart to this day.

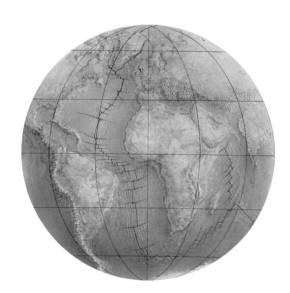

400 Million Years
Final closure of the Iapetus Ocean complete. The continents collide like 'ghostly ships in the fog'. Baltica collides head-on with Laurentia, whereas Avalonia 'docks' gently to the south.

Setting the Scene

The geological make up of the Northwest Highlands ranges from some of the oldest, most altered rocks in Britain to the eroded roots of the Skye volcano, a mere 60 million years old! Most recently, a thin patchy veneer of sand, gravel and clay was left by the melting ice. The main rock units are aligned in a north-northeasterly direction, and this grain is in turn reflected in the landscape. Approaching from the east, high peat-clad moorland is encountered, with clusters of rugged peaks. All are built of altered or metamorphic rocks, the Moine Schists. Descending from the watershed towards the west coast, more isolated, tiered and buttressed mountains command attention. Slioch, Beinn Eighe and

Liathach stand out in Torridon, An Teallach and Ben More Coigach around Loch Broom, and Suilven and Quinag in Assynt. They are composed of Torridonian Sandstone and some have caps of white Cambrian Quartzite. They overlook hummocky and very rocky terrain composed of Lewisian Gneiss, which stretches to the coast.

The Highlands of Scotland were created both during and following the closure of the Iapetus Ocean. This closure took place over some 80 million years, as Laurentia, the continent of which Scotland was part, collided with a variety of other land masses. When crustal plates collide, one of the plates is normally pushed deep within the Earth, often as far as 100km in depth. This causes the plate to become hot and the increased temperatures and pressures change the original sediments and volcanic rocks to metamorphic rocks. The sediments caught up in the collision are lighter than the surrounding deep crust and mantle rocks, so once the downward motion has ceased, the metamorphosed rocks rise upwards at rates of around a centimetre each year. The Highlands of Scotland owe their origin to these events, which culminated some 420 million years ago, when Scotland, England and Scandinavia, formerly separated by the Iapetus Ocean, were united to form a single area of continental crust.

Lewisian Gneiss fringing Loch Laxford

The Early Crust

A typical 'Lewisian' landscape - Loch Laxford

Some of the Earth's most ancient rocks are to be found in the Northwest Highlands. Most are known as gneisses, which are characteristically layered rocks forged in the furnace of the lower reaches of the Earth's crust. Originally they were predominantly igneous intrusions - grey to pink granitic rocks, dark grey base-rich gabbros and related rocks. These intrusions formed by localised melting of the mantle rocks beneath the Earth's crust and the molten rocks subsequently rose into the lower parts of the crust, as they were less dense than the rocks that surrounded them. Complex mountain building movements also occurred at around the same time.

The configuration of continents on the Earth at that time bore no resemblance to that of today. Although many of the geological processes that formed these ancient rocks remain obscure, it seems likely that Northwest Scotland was linked to Canada, Greenland and northern Scandinavia as rocks similar to the Lewisian Gneisses occur in these countries. Evidence suggests that the continental plates that existed when the early crust was forming were smaller than present and that heat flow from the core of the Earth to the surface was higher as a result of the greater abundance and enhanced decay of radioactive minerals.

It was the movement of crustal plates that caused part of the crust to be deeply buried. The resulting intense pressure and heating to over 650°C transformed the rocks into gneisses around 2600 million years ago. There followed a long history of gradual uplift and erosion, punctuated by further earth movements until they finally reached the surface about 1100 million years ago. The rocks we now see at the surface today thus record events which mainly took place some 15 to 30km deep in the Earth's crust.

Lewisian Gneisses are remarkably diverse in character, reflecting the variety of rocks from which they were formed. Granitic and gabbroic intrusions derived from the upper mantle, ancient sediments, including muds and limestones, and a thick sequence of lavas erupted some 2000 million years ago were all altered and amalgamated to create the ancient crust. The most ancient gneisses were cut by a dense swarm of intrusions of basic molten rock, known as dykes, and later by granite sheets. The resultant kaleidoscopic variety of rocks which were formed over such an extended period of geological time is widely regarded as one of the highlights of Scottish geology.

Lewisian Gneiss - dark basic dykes cut older pale grey gneisses and are in turn cross-cut by granite veins

Rivers of Sand

Glen Torridon - tiered hills of
Torridonian Sandstone beds

By 1100 million years ago, over 15km of early crust had been eroded from Northwest Scotland, mainly under tropical semi-desert conditions. Then, the gneisses were buried once again, this time under a carpet of sands and gravels. Periodic rainfall eroded the remaining upstanding areas of Lewisian Gneiss which stood up to 2km higher than the broad valleys bounded by large faults. Sands, gravels and mud were laid down, both in fans that spread out from the higher ground, and also more abundantly in wide river channels and ephemeral lakes. At least 7km of these Torridonian sediments mainly derived from Labrador and the Canadian Shield smothered the ancient crust. At Cape Wrath the sandstones forming the cliffs are part of a single large alluvial fan deposit some 450m thick that extends as far south as Quinag in Assynt.

Two separate sequences of Torridonian rocks are distinguished. The older sequence up to 2km thick is composed of angular rock debris, sandstone and shale. It contains a distinctive volcanic muddy sandstone horizon which can be recognised from Poolewe northwards to Stoer. The younger sequence, well-developed in Cape Wrath, Torridon and the area around Applecross is up to 6km thick and consists of red-brown to purple, coarse-grained sandstones and minor conglomerates and shales. Their widely jointed nature and thick beds makes them resistant to weathering and mechanical erosion. Their current sculpted form is a product of scouring by ice but 'Torridonian' mountains have been upstanding areas for many millions of years.

This once continuous blanket of Torridonian Sandstones deposited on the eroded Lewisian landscape has been largely eroded over time. Thus, in places, the original land surface that existed over a billion years ago has been exhumed and the landscape we see today is indeed an ancient one. Had we stood here a billion years ago, the contours of the Lewisian Gneiss would have been uncannily similar to those of today.

Slioch - Torridonian sandstones infill a 'Lewisian' valley

Early Life on Earth

**The mountains of Arkle and
Foinaven - capped by quartzite**

About 545 million years ago, at the time when animals with backbones were first becoming widely distributed around the world, Northwest Scotland lay at the edge of the Laurentian continent. It formed part of a wide, stable, low-lying area, gradually eroded down to a near horizontal surface over the previous 250 million years. The earliest deposits from this Cambrian age, were clean, quartz-rich, sands, laid down by vigorous tidal currents in tropical, shallow seas and intertidal zones. The upper part of the resulting sand deposit was colonised by marine worms and impressions of their burrows are very abundant, giving it the name 'Pipe Rock'. The sands were subsequently altered to quartzite, a hard and in places a brilliantly white rock that forms a prominent cap to several of the higher peaks, such as Arkle, Foinaven, An Teallach, Beinn Eighe, Liathach, Canisp and Quinag.

The quartzite is overlain by brown to orange, potash-rich, dolomitic silts and muds containing abundant remains of small mats of algae. The rocks are called the Fucoid Beds, as they were initially thought to contain seaweed impressions (fucoids). They are now known to be worm trails, formed as these animals buried through the soft sediment. Some of the earliest fossils of hard-bodied creatures found in Britain occur here - trilobites, and the ancestors of snails, cockles and sea-urchins. Above the Fucoid Beds, which only reach about 20m in thickness, lies the Salterella Grit. This gritty quartzite and dolomitic sandstone bed contains very abundant remains of the early 'snail', Salterella, in its upper parts. The highest units in this sequence are composed of Durness limestones and

Green pastures underlain
by limestone - Elphin

dolomites, with some chert nodules. They vary from white to dark grey and individual limestone units can be traced from Durness to Skye. Colonies of algae have also been recognised in these strata. The upper parts are of early Ordovician age, formed about 490 million years ago, and the limestones appear to represent a span of about 30 to 40 million years. Even where no rock is exposed, the presence of the limestones and dolomites is still evident from the bright green grassy pastures and more varied flora typical of calcareous soils.

Pipe rock - worm
burrows in ancient
beach sand

Continents Collide

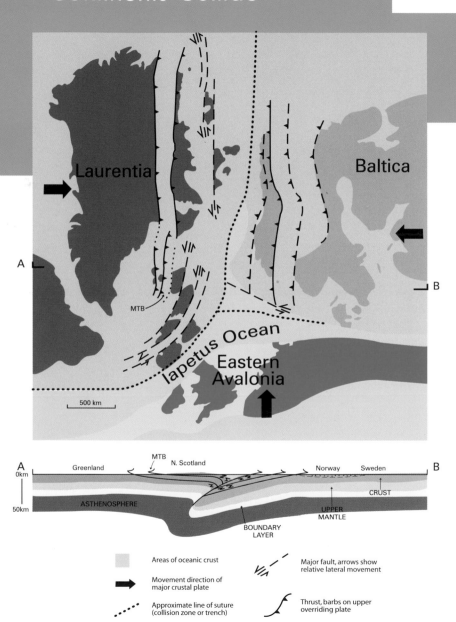

Iapetus closure with collision of
Laurentia and Baltica and
'docking' of Eastern Avalonia

Laurentia

Baltica

MTB

Iapetus Ocean

Eastern
Avalonia

500 km

A · · · · MTB · · · N. Scotland · · · · · · · · · · · Norway · · Sweden · · · · · · · · B
0km
Greenland
CRUST
ASTHENOSPHERE
50km
BOUNDARY
LAYER
UPPER
MANTLE

Areas of oceanic crust

Movement direction of
major crustal plate

Approximate line of suture
(collision zone or trench)

Major fault, arrows show
relative lateral movement

Thrust, barbs on upper
overriding plate

The sedimentary rocks previously described that had accumulated over about 500 million years on the margin of Laurentia were folded and buckled as the Iapetus Ocean finally closed. In Scotland great wedges of rock were thrust westwards over the ancient Lewisian crust, as the effects of the collision radiated far and wide. At times high mountains formed, as the continents ploughed into each other squeezing the sea floor and beach sediments as if in the jaws of a vice. At least 70km of crust was over-ridden, as the 'screw tightened' and wedges of rock, each separated from the one below by a fault or thrust, stacked up and moved westwards. When thrust movement ceased due to increased frictional resistance, a new plane of weakness developed at a lower level and thrusting movement concentrated there. The older thrust was then transported 'piggy-back' on the new dislocation until it in turn became stalled. The Moine Thrust Belt, which runs from Loch Eriboll on the north coast southwards to near Kyle of Lochalsh and into Skye contains a mixture of

Moine Thrust
at Knockan Crag

Lewisian, Torridonian and Cambrian rocks that were thrust together as continents collided. Its surface outcrop varies in width from a few hundred metres near Ullapool to 11km wide in Assynt. It represents one of the most earth-shattering events that took place in our three billion year history and has attracted the interest of geologists for well over a century.

Knockan Crag is one of the best locations to appreciate the great forces that must have been at work. Older metamorphosed schistose Moine rocks have been driven over the Cambrian limestones and quartzites. At the contact, the rock was ground down, smashed and broken as the upper layers moved inexorably westward.

Geological cross-section showing Moine Schists overriding the stacked younger Cambrian rocks along the Moine Thrust

Fusion of poetry and scenery "... I don't remember the eagle going away. But I'll never forget the eagle-shaped space it left, stamped in the air". Norman MacCaig *In Everything*

Come to Knockan Crag and discover the planet! A visitor attraction has been created at Knockan Crag, 20km north of Ullapool, that tells the story of part of Scotland's turbulent geological past. Global processes have been at work to create the unique rock formations and spectacular landscapes at this historic site. The story is told using poetry, sculpture, interactive demonstations and cartoons, which illustrate the drama of past geological events and the people involved in unravelling this fascinating story.

Sculptures on the trail

Concepts etched in stone

Visit the Knockan website and make sure that you get a copy of the teachers pack if you would like to visit Knockan with a student party. Walk the geological trail and admire the superb views of Assynt.

website: www: knockan-crag.co.uk

Satellite Sites Around Assynt

View across Loch Glencoul to the Glencoul Thrust

Interpretation panels have been installed at twelve geologically important sites around the Assynt. We point the way to the bone caves south of Inchnadamph, explain some of the spectacular views, e.g. Loch Glencoul, and find the place where Ben Peach and John Horne stayed when they were undertaking their survey of the Northwest Highlands. Join us on a geological safari around Assynt!

Glacial erratics near Rhiconich

Interpretative panels at a roadside cutting near Laxford Bridge

Molten Masses

Granites are common throughout the Highlands, but are absent from the far Northwest Highlands. Here, the only large intrusions present are those found in Assynt, and these are formed of syenite, a grey to pink, coarse-grained feldspar-rich rock. The syenites formed by localised melting of the Earth's mantle and the resulting magma subsequently rose and crystallised at shallow levels in the crust at around 440 to 430 million years ago. The intrusions form misshapen balloon-like bodies up to 5km across, and have associated offshoots which radiate outwards in thin sheets of previously molten rock, called dykes and sills. Many contain distinctive and unusual minerals. Some of these unique rock types were first described from Assynt and were given local names such as boralanite, assyntite, ledmoreite and cromaltite.

Marble at Ledmore Quarry

Exposures of syenite

Pale grey weathering sill in dark grey
dolomitic limestones at Inchnadamph

The syenites form the lower ground and small rounded hills in Assynt, with the two main intrusions centred on Loch Borralan and Loch Ailsh. As the syenite rose from the depths of the Earth, it came into contact with Cambrian limestones. The heat radiated by the syenite, which was at about 700°C, turned the limestone into marble, and caused new minerals and exotic rock types to be developed where the syenite made contact with the limestones.

These igneous intrusions of Assynt are important to the story of the Moine Thrust Zone in that their injection into the thrust melange apparently happened coincident with these earth movements. The age of the intrusions has been worked out by studying the radioactive decay pattern of uranium to lead in zircons crystals contained in the syenite. This allows the major movements of the Moine Thrust Zone to be dated accurately at 430 million years.

The Age of Ice

Glaciers at work today at Margerie Glacier, Glacier Bay National Park, Alaska - the landscape of the Northwest Highlands was shaped by ice in a similar fashion 12,000 years ago

Little is known about most of the last 430 million years since the continents collided. Like detectives, geologists need evidence, but unfortunately there were few younger rocks deposited and even less are preserved in the Northwest Highlands. However, it is known that the main elements of the landscape were in place by Tertiary times, around 65 million years ago. There were isolated massifs of Torridonian sandstone, a low-lying plain developed on Lewisian gneiss, and a westward facing escarpment along the Moine Thrust Zone. River valleys extended eastwards from this watershed towards the Moray Firth. Volcanoes erupted to the south, the largest on Skye and Mull. The climate during Tertiary times was subtropical, but around 5 million years ago the temperature began to fall.

At the beginning of what is popularly known as the Ice Age, some 2.4 million years ago, the climate cooled more dramatically. Major cycles of climatic change began. Initially, cold episodes, during which mountain corrie glaciers probably first appeared, were separated by shorter warm episodes every 40,000 years or so. The climatic fluctuation then later became more extreme and since about 750,000 years ago there have been long, intensely cold 'glacial' episodes separated by short, warm 'interglacials' at roughly 100,000 year intervals. Most of the soils, sediments and weathered rocks which had formed during the Tertiary Period were swept away by ice in these major glaciations. Cave systems developed in the limestones of the Inchnadamph area during early glacial and interglacial episodes, before the valleys had been eroded to their present depths and when the water table was some 150m higher than today. It is known from radiometric dating of stalagmites in caves near Inchnadamph that ice-free conditions occurred in the region during the last interglacial period, around 122,000 years ago, and again between about 40,000 and 29,000 years ago.

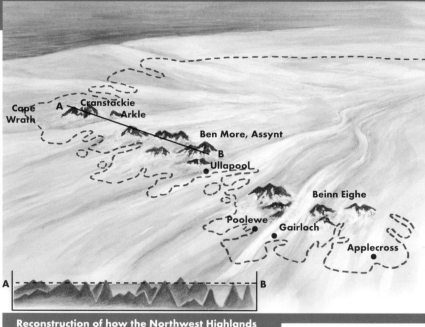

Reconstruction of how the Northwest Highlands may have looked during the last major glaciation

The last widespread major glaciation began about 29,000 years ago when glaciers grew and coalesced to form an ice-sheet over Scotland. By 22,000 years ago it had enveloped all but the highest pinnacles of mountains such as An Teallach and swept away most of the older glacial deposits. The ice cap then dwindled in size slowly and, following a sudden climatic warming about 14,700 years ago, it started to melt very quickly indeed. For a thousand years or so summer temperatures were similar to those we have today, but the climate then cooled again. By 12,500 years ago, a tundra environment had returned and arctic conditions again prevailed.

During a final minor glaciation, a large ice field extended as far north as Torridon, with outlet glaciers descending close to present sea level. There were numerous valley and corrie glaciers in the mountains farther to the north. The surrounding areas were frozen wastes, similar to those found today in parts of Arctic Europe, Asia and Canada.

Some 11,500 years ago, the climate warmed very rapidly indeed, heralding the beginning of the present interglacial period. The glaciers melted quickly and vegetation soon returned to stabilise the soils.

The Main Glaciation

A large glacial erratic boulder near Loch Laxford

The Ice Age has left an indelible imprint on the landscape of the Northwest Highlands. It is largely responsible for its rugged and desolate beauty. Evidence from scratch marks on the bedrock, known as striae, and rocks carried from their original outcrops by ice, called glacial erratics, enable us to reconstruct where the ice flowed during the last major glaciation. Large areas of frost-shattered rock created during earlier intense cold periods occur on some mountaintops. These stood above the last ice sheet, like nunataks do today in Greenland. The blockfields are commonly sharply bounded from ice-scoured slopes lower on the mountainside. The boundaries, called glacial trimlines, record the maximum altitude of the ice sheet. The ice sheet reached about 950m altitude along the present watershed. It descended northwards and north-westwards into the Minch, sweeping around the

Torridonian mountains, breaching watersheds, scouring away loose and weathered rocks, over-deepening, widening and straightening pre-existing valleys. The ice flowed out at least 100km from the present coast through fjords like Loch Hourn and Loch Broom, although huge features such as these must have been pre-existing valleys and have been partially gouged out during previous glaciations.

When the ice melted, it released the rock fragments it had carried to form hummocky spreads of gravelly debris. Glaciers periodically re-advanced to create moraine ridges. A particularly fine end-moraine lies to the north of Gairloch and it can be traced along much of the seaboard of Wester Ross.

The valley of Loch Broom, once an ice-gouged fjord, is now partially filled with river sediments

A Warm Interlude and the Final Glaciation

Corrie of a Hundred Hills

The climate warmed up at about 14,700 years ago, when most, if not all of the ice sheet melted. The freshly exposed stony soils were soon colonised by pioneer vegetation such as grasses, sedges, clubmosses, 'alpine' herbs and dwarf willow. Next came a mosaic of juniper scrub, crowberry, heather, grassland and birchwood. But this warmer spell was short lived. The climate deteriorated and snow accumulated again. A short glaciation followed when ice once more plucked, scoured, carved and polished the ancient rocks of the district. In this minor glaciation the corries of An Teallach supported glaciers, forming end-moraines up to 40m high, and a valley glacier reached the sea at the head of Loch Kishorn.

Freeze-thaw 'periglacial' processes were particularly active on the mountain tops during this last glaciation (Loch Lomond Re-advance). On steeper slopes, the loosened boulders and soil crept downhill to form distinctive lobes, sheets and terracettes of debris.

Two particularly interesting landforms of the region formed at this time. On Baosbheinn, a ridge built of rock fragments formed at the base of a snowbank through the accumulation of rock debris that fell from cliffs above. Ridges formed in this way are called 'protalus ramparts'. On Beinn Alligin, a large rockfall occurred that showered debris on to the surface of a glacier at the foot of the mountain. When the glacier melted a labyrinth of huge boulders was left behind.

On melting, the glaciers left behind widespread hummocky moraines, such as in Coire a' Cheud-chnoic, which in Gaelic means Corrie of a Hundred Hills. They also left the ice-plucked corrie head walls and needle-sharp ridges (arêtes) that now provide some of the most challenging climbing in Scotland. Screes formed in the corries as frost-shattered rocks continued to tumble down from the cliffs and gullies.

The 'U'-shaped valley looking from Bealach na Bà towards Kishorn

The Bone Caves of Inchnadamph

Lynx, wolf, bear and reindeer - all former inhabitants of this part of Scotland

During wetter and warmer periods of the Ice Age, groundwaters dissolved away the fractured, white, dolomitic Cambrian Durness limestones to create a system of underground caves and narrow passages. Some of these, such as the now dry cave at Creag nan Uamh (Crag of the Caves) provided a refuge for animals during the last glaciation, and perhaps also for humans. Many bones have been discovered in the deeper recesses of the caves including those of brown bear, arctic fox, northern lynx, arctic lemming and wolf. Reindeer antlers are most numerous and they have yielded radiocarbon dates of between 9,000 and 44,000 years before present. Some experts maintain that the antler remains, which are mostly shed antler burrs, could only have been brought into the cave by humans, making this the oldest archaeological site in Scotland. Others disagree and think that the remains were washed in naturally from a nearby reindeer calving ground.

The 'cave earth' in the entrance chambers formed during the last 10,000 years or so. A fragment of human skull indicates that humans were present. The bones of animals such as bears and wolves, no longer living in Scotland today, remind us that these species owe their extinction to humans rather than to the changing climate.

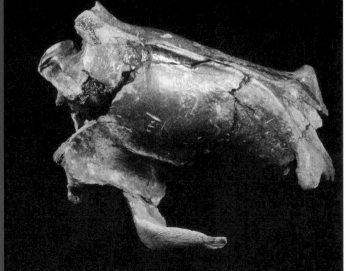

Remains of a lynx skull (left) and part of a polar bear skull (above) found in the caves at Inchnadamph

After the Ice

Many changes in the style of landscape evolution were brought about 11,500 years ago by the sudden switch from a severe glacial climate to a relatively warm one dominated by the Gulf Stream. The most profound change was the return of vegetation to stabilise the soils. An initial pioneer community of plants was soon replaced by dwarf-shrub tundra. A heather and juniper-dominated phase then gave way at about 10,000 years ago to mixed birch and hazel woodland. Oak and elm subsequently became established in sheltered positions in the south of the area and Scots pine had arrived around Loch Maree by about 9,000 years ago. Alder arrived much later. Reduction in the forest cover and expansion of blanket peat began when the climate became cooler and wetter some 6,000 years ago. People may have begun to fell trees to plant crops at this time, but extensive clearance of forest probably did not begin until about 1,500 years ago.

Scots pines have been a prominent element of the Highland landscape for the past 9,000 years

**Scree slopes and debris cones
of Quartzite on Foinaven**

Although glaciers are no longer present, mountain summits continue to be affected by freeze-thaw processes and anyone venturing into the hills can observe a range of active periglacial landforms. These include stone stripes and circles, turf-banked terraces, 'ploughing' boulders, wind-eroded surfaces and wind patterning of vegetation. These modern phenomena can be distinguished from the larger scale, fossil features formed during the glacial periods.

Other indications of our dynamic environment include the gullies that snake down many mountainsides, caused by debris flows and landslides after heavy rainfall, and by snow avalanches. The eroded material often forms cone-like piles of debris at the base of slopes. Such erosion appears to be increasing, but whether this is due to grazing activity or recent climatic change is not certain.

The Coastline

Smoo Cave

The remote, rugged, fjord-indented coastline of the Northwest Highlands has suffered relentless attack by the sea over many thousands of years since the last glaciers retreated. Atlantic waves pound against towering, vertical cliffs of Torridonian Sandstone along long stretches of the outer coastline, but in a few locations sandy beaches nestle in sheltered bays. Elsewhere, intertidal mud flats and salt marshes have formed in the more sheltered environments, such as at the heads of sea lochs. It is here also that rivers have dumped their burden of sand and pebbles over the ages, building up alluvial fans and deltas. The free-draining ground on such features has provided sought-after cultivable land in a landscape dominated by rock and bog.

Sandwood Bay

Along the westward-facing coastline the awesome power of the Atlantic waves has carved out spectacular caves and sea stacks, especially where joints and cracks in the rock lie at high angles to the shore. A wave entering a crevice compresses air tightly within it. When the wave recedes, the compressed air expands violently loosening rocks in the cliff wall and blowing out fragments bodily, until eventually a cave is formed. When two caves on opposite sides of a headland unite, a natural arch may be created for a while, before it collapses and the seaward portion of the headland becomes a sea stack. In other circumstances, the combined bombardment and blasting by the waves produces long, narrow tidal inlets called geos. More rarely, a vertical chimney forms in the roof of a cave at the landward end of a geo. During storms, sea spray is ejected forcibly through the blow hole or 'gloup' so formed. A similar-looking feature occurs at Smoo, where a stream descends through a swallow hole into a cave below. Here the combined attack by the sea and the river has dissolved away the Durness limestones to create a large cavern.

One of the most spectacular coastal walks in Britain is from Cape Wrath to Sandwood Bay, from which a wide range of features of marine erosion can be seen. Farther south on Handa Island, bedding planes in the Torridonian Sandstone have been etched out by the elements to provide resting places for countless seabirds. In contrast to these rugged and desolate stretches of coast, sandy beaches favoured by holiday makers nestle in sheltered bays such as at Gairloch. Here the beach sand, which contains a large proportion of calcareous shell fragments, has been blown inland to form dunes covered by a grassy sward similar to the machair of the Western Isles.

**Sea stack -
Old Man of Stoer**

Ancient Beaches

Applecross - the platform behind the cliff line was cut when sea level was much higher than today

Long abandoned beaches and wave-cut platforms lying up to 40m above sea level are common along the coasts of Applecross and Wester Ross, gently declining in altitude northwards. Most of them formed from about 16,000 years ago as the late Devensian ice sheet in Scotland decayed. At this time sea level was relatively high in Scotland even though the world's oceans were partly locked up in great continental ice sheets and sea level at the equator was 100 metres lower than today. The high sea levels occurred because the Earth's crust had locally sagged under the weight of the several kilometres thick Scottish ice sheet.

A further set of raised and tilted beaches are found at heights of up to 9m above high water mark. They are most common at the head of sea lochs such as Loch Broom and Loch Carron. The beaches formed between 8,000 and 5,000 years ago during a period of rapid rise in world sea level caused by the melting of ice sheets in North America and Scandinavia, but before Scotland had completely recovered from the unloading of its former ice cover. The raised beaches all tilt gently owing to varying amounts of uplift since the ice melted.

Gruinard Bay - a raised beach
backs the present shore

The Landscape Today

A long and winding road - Beinne Stach in the background

It is the geology that gives rise to the dramatic landscapes we experience in Northwest Scotland today. Here we can move between the seemingly impenetrable mass of high hills, witness the drama of mountains climbing steeply out of long deep sea lochs and contemplate solitary peaks rising unexpectedly from the gently undulating knoc and lochan landscape, a rocky surface peppered with tiny lochans. The scenery is some of the finest in Scotland, with two thirds being designated as a nationally significant scenic resource.

However, life is sometimes hard here - the conditions are exposed and the terrain difficult to traverse or cultivate, leaving the area very sparsely populated. Settlement is focused where the land meets the sea, as people typically make a living by combining cultivation of the flatter, less stony ground with harvesting produce from the sea. Sheltered harbours such as Gairloch, Lochinver and Ullapool can be found along this coast, which is punctuated by scattered offshore islands and sandy bays and characterised by often stunning views of the more distant islands. The indented coastal landform also creates sheltered niches for small areas of broadleaf woodland to flourish away from the harsh, salt laden winds.

Further inland, settlement concentrates around the richer limestone based soils of areas such as Elphin and at the confluences of the major glens such as Kinlochewe. Here the the bright green winter grazing fields of

the in-bye land, which are nearest the settlement, contrast starkly with the surrounding sombre heather moorland that traditionally provides sparse summer grazing for sheep and deer and peat for winter fuel.

Although a few roads have greatly facilitated access, much of Northwest Scotland remains relatively inaccessible, with the high relief and the mass of the mountains forcing roads to follow the flatter coastal areas. Places seem farther apart than they really are, as it takes a long time to travel short distances on narrow, winding roads. While the vegetation pattern is strongly influenced by human intervention, and there is evidence that there was more extensive habitation in the past, today this area is perceived to be a largely natural landscape. Large tracts of land are accessible only on foot and a sense of remoteness and quiet prevails.

Lochinver - a sheltered natural harbour

Scottish Natural Heritage
and the British Geological Survey

Scottish Natural Heritage is a government body. Its aim is to help people enjoy Scotland's natural heritage responsibly, understand it more fully and use it wisely so that it can be sustained for future generations.

Scottish Natural Heritage
Great Glen House, Leachkin Road
Inverness IV3 8NW

SCOTTISH NATURAL HERITAGE

The British Geological Survey maintains up-to-date knowledge of the geology of the UK and its continental shelf. It carries out surveys and geological research.
The Scottish Office of BGS is sited in Edinburgh. The office runs an advisory and information service, a geological library and a well-stocked geological bookshop.

British Geological Survey
Murchison House
West Mains Road
Edinburgh EH9 3LA

British Geological Survey
NATURAL ENVIRONMENT RESEARCH COUNCIL

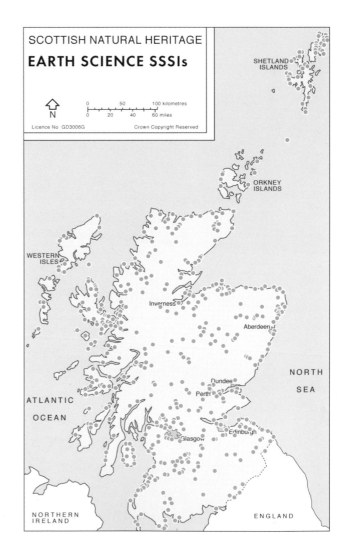

SCOTTISH NATURAL HERITAGE
EARTH SCIENCE SSSIs

N

| 0 | 50 | 100 kilometres |
| 0 | 20 | 40 | 60 miles |

Licence No GD3006G   Crown Copyright Reserved

SHETLAND ISLANDS

ORKNEY ISLANDS

WESTERN ISLES

Inverness

Aberdeen

Dundee

Perth

NORTH SEA

ATLANTIC OCEAN

Edinburgh

Glasgow

NORTHERN IRELAND

ENGLAND

Remember the Geological Code!

SCOTTISH NATURAL HERITAGE

Keep collecting to a minimum: remove fossils, rocks or minerals only when essential for serious study. And remember to refer good finds to local museums.

No need to hammer indiscriminately! Never collect from walls or buildings.

The leader of a field party should ensure that the spirit of the code is upheld.

Always seek permission before entering private land.

No one has the right to "dig out" any site. Try to leave the site as you found it!

Don't litter fields or roads with rock fragments, and avoid disturbing plants or wildlife.

Back fill excavations where necessary to avoid injury to people or animals.

Be considerate, and do not make things more difficult or hazardous for others coming after you.

Don't disfigure rock surfaces with brightly painted numbers, symbols or clusters of core-holes.

SAFETY FIRST!
✔ Wear protective goggles when hammering.
✔ Wear safety hats in quarries or below cliffs.
✔ Avoid loosening rocks on steep slopes.
✗ Do not get cut off by the tide.
✗ Do not enter old mine workings or cave systems.
✗ Do not interfere with machinery in quarries.

● Remember, you are one of several hundred geologists visiting this area every year — so your behaviour *does* matter.
● Please observe the code, so that others can also enjoy the great scenery, geology, and ecology here!

Published by Scottish Natural Heritage, 1996.

Also in the Landscape Fashioned by Geology series...

If you have enjoyed Northwest Highlands why not find out more about the geology of some of Scotland's distinctive areas in our Landscape Fashioned by Geology series. Each book helps you to explore what lies beneath the soils, trees and heather with clear explanations, stunning photographs and illustrations. The series, which is produced in collaboration with the British Geological Survey, is written by experts in a style which is accessible to all.

Arran and the Clyde Islands

The diverse landscapes of Arran and the Clyde Islands mark the boundary between Highland and Lowland. Discover the ancient secrets and the appeal of these well-loved islands.
David McAdam & Steve Robertson
ISBN 1 85397 287 8 pbk 24pp £3.00

East Lothian and the Borders

Underneath the calm facade of south east Scotland's fertile plains and rolling hills lies a complex structure, which reflects an eventful geological history.
David McAdam & Phil Stone
ISBN 1 85397 242 8 pbk 26pp £3.00

Fife and Tayside

The dramatic coastline and volcanic hills of Fife and Tayside are testament to the dramatic geological past. The story is set at a time when Scotland sat astride the equator.
Mike Browne, Alan McKirdy & David McAdam
ISBN 1 85397 110 3 pbk 36pp £3.95

Loch Lomond to Stirling

The heart of Scotland encompasses some of the most diverse landscapes in Scotland. From the low Carse to the mountain tops - find out how these modern landscapes reflect the geological changes of the past.
Mike Browne & John Mendum
ISBN 1 85397 119 7 pbk 26pp £2.00

Orkney and Shetland

These northern outposts of Scotland hold a great fascination for the geologist. Starting 3 billion years ago, their story tells of colliding continents, bizarre lifeforms and a landscape which continues to be eroded by the pounding force of the Atlantic.
Clive Auton, Terry Fletcher & David Gould
ISBN 1 85397 220 7 pbk 24pp £2.50

Skye

Skye is one of Scotland's most popular tourist destinations, and deservedly so. But what would Skye be without the jagged peaks of the Cuillins or the intriguing rock formations of the Quirang? In many ways it is the geology of Skye that attracts it's visitors and this booklet helps you to understand how the mountains, rocks and lochs were formed.
David Stephenson & Jon Merritt
ISBN 1 85397 026 3 pbk 24pp £2.50

Scotland: the creation of its natural landscape

Scotland: the Creation of its Natural Landscape provides a wealth of information on how Scotland was created and the events that took place there through the aeons. But the story doesn't stop back in the mists of time, it continually unfolds and this book provides up to the minute information on geological events taking place beneath our feet, It also provides a history of geological science and highlights the enormous contribution Scots geologists have made to the world.
Alan McKirdy and Roger Crofts
ISBN 1 85397 004 2 pbk 64pp £7.50

Series Editor: Alan McKirdy (SNH)

SNH Publication Order Form

Title	Price	Quantity
Arran & the Clyde Islands	£3.00	
East Lothian & the Borders	£3.00	
Fife & Tayside	£3.95	
Loch Lomond to Stirling	£2.00	
Orkney & Shetland	£2.50	
Skye	£3.95	
Scotland: the Creation of its natural landscape	£7.50	

Postage and packaging: free of charge within the UK.

A standard charge of £2.95 will be applied to all orders from the EU.

Elsewhere a standard charge of £5.50 will apply.

Please complete in **BLOCK CAPITALS**

Name _____

Address _____

_____

Post Code _____

Type of Credit Card VISA ☐   MasterCard ☐

Name of card holder _____

Card Number ☐☐☐☐ ☐☐☐☐ ☐☐☐☐ ☐☐☐☐

Expiry Date ☐☐ ☐☐

Send order and cheque made payable to Scottish Natural Heritage to:

Scottish Natural Heritage, Design and Publications, Battleby, Redgorton, Perth PH1 3EW

E-mail: pubs@snh.gov.uk www.snh.org.uk